QUANTUM
PHYSICS
FOR BEGINNERS

From Wave Theory to Quantum Computing.
Understanding How Everything Works by a
Simplified Explanation of Quantum Physics and
Mechanics Principles

CARL J. PRATT

IPPOCERONTE
publishing

Table of Contents

Introduction

So, you've heard about quantum physics, and you want to understand better what it is, right? Let me start by saying that I admire your curiosity and dedication to learning. Quantum physics has become one of the biggest trends in the last decades. Even if we are not physicists and we have zero interaction with whatever is mathematical or scientific, we may have read about it in the newspaper or heard it in movies or TV comedies. Still, even if we heard about it, not everybody would take the effort to approach such a tricky subject. So, congratulations on taking the first step and getting involved in this world. Don't worry if you have no physics background because I wrote the book for everybody curious about the quantum universe, so you don't need to be a scientist to understand the concepts explained in this text. Allow me now to answer some of the questions you may have about the main subject of this book before we start.

What is quantum physics? Is it different from the physics we studied at school when we were teenagers or younger? Absolutely. Quantum physics is the latest achievement in the scientific world, and it has the potential to explain how everything works, from atoms to black holes. Why do I say so? *quantum* is a Latin word correlated with "quantity," and *quanta* are the smallest amount of any physical entity. The term suggests that quantum physics studies the material at the most minimal scale to understand how particles work and interact with each other. It underlies how atoms work and why chemistry and biology work as they do. As you can see, everything, including our bodies, is involved at some levels with particles and forces with which they interact. For this reason, quantum physics is often described as *the science that explains everything*.

But to find an answer to every possible question in the world where we live, experiments proved that we couldn't stay attached to the fundamentals of classical physics. We had to bring some innovation and break some of the rules that we take for granted. We must watch the law of physics with new eyes if we want to expand our horizons to new knowledge. So, to answer the previous questions, no: Quantum physics and classical physics have nothing in common; for this reason, this topic may sound difficult for people who are not directly involved in science. However, we have learned that mathematics has no objections, and physics has no space for doubts. Well, we can't approach the quantum world with this set of mind. If we want to understand this topic truly, we must ignore what we have learned so far and prepare our minds to embrace probabilities and paradoxes. It may be challenging initially, but I assure you that it's worth trying.

I collected the most significant achievements that helped quantum physics grow in this book. I tried to keep everything chronologically to give you an idea of the history and evolution of this topic. I did my best to keep the text as straightforward as possible, but I had to apply some formulas with a mathematical explanation for you to have a better understanding of the subject. If you are not interested in the mathematical proof, you can skip those parts, and the book should still give you a historical point of view of the events that happened in the world of quantum physics. Now, let's get deeper into this exciting topic.

~ Part 1 ~
First Steps in Quantum Physics

1.1 What Is Quantum Physics?

Quantum physics is a branch of physics that deals with physical phenomena at microscopic scales. It specifically describes the behavior of infinitely small objects working with distances at times shorter than the diameter of an atom.

Put simply; it's the physics that explains how everything works: The best description we have of the nature of the particles that make up matter and the forces with which they interact.

This science has revealed a whole new aspect of reality, one not directly observable with the human eye and senses alone. This new universe is one of radical uncertainty and pure energy. It contradicts our common sense, yet it is the most comprehensive and successful theory in all of science. Modern technology, such as computers, lasers, and transistors, are based on quantum physics since it was first discovered.

This subject helps us build better computers and enable future technology that seems entirely science fiction. It also provides the foundations to understand how objects react with each other on a microscopic level.

Quantum physics differs fundamentally from classical physics at its core.

Let's look at how the cornerstone principles differ in these two disciplines:

- According to Newton's first law of motion, "an object should have a definite position and momentum at all times." However, according to Heisenberg's uncertainty principle, one of the subatomic particles, such as electrons, does not have a well-defined position or momentum (1927).

- A classical object has a definite mass. However, electrons have a variable and not a well-defined mass.

- A classical object has a definite velocity. However, electrons do not have a well-defined velocity; they just have a probability of being at various locations in space.

- In quantum mechanics, the properties of an object are represented by mathematical objects called wave functions. The uncertainty principle implies that even if you know all the components of a particle's wave function, you still don't know its location and momentum with complete accuracy. The position and momentum of an object are not determined until it is observed (so an observer becomes part of the system).

The uncertainty principle and wave functions are concepts that seem absurd at first, and many people became very confused by these notions. However, once you start to understand the core principles of quantum physics and think about the implications of these ideas, everything becomes clearer and, in some cases, intuitive.

1.2 *Some Essential Characteristics of Quantum Physics*

Don't worry if some of these concepts are still obscure to you; we will have time to explore them in more detail in later chapters.

For now, I just want you to start getting familiar with some of the core features of quantum physics:

- Atoms, electrons, photons, etc., are not actually particles; they are 'quanta' of various things (energy, mass, etc.). In fact, according to quantum physics, matter exists in small indivisible packets called *quanta*.

- The quantum physical world is very different from our 'everyday' world. It is a strange universe where particles can be in two places at once, and objects can disappear and reappear in a new place without having traveled there in between.

- Nothing happens in the quantum physical world unless somebody or something observes it. In other words, even if an event occurs (say, a photon emitted by an atom), it will not happen, until there is an observer present to measure the event.

- Time is not a constant quantity in the quantum physical world but comes in discrete jumps. For example, one second can be equal to one hour in "quantum time."

- There is such a thing as 'negative' energy in the quantum physical world, which has the same magnitude as positive energy. This negative energy must be added to the positive energy to find the total energy of a particle or system (a fundamental law called "conservation of energy").

I know, I know, it seems all vague now. But, let's start from the basics, and I promise you that everything will make sense!

~ Part 2 ~

What Exactly Is Light?

2.1 and There Was Light

Before we leave classical physics behind us, we need to know a few things about light so that we can go deeper into the quantum physics realm.

Light will be the protagonist of many important (and at first puzzling) issues when we start to enter the quantum world. So, we will now take a historical look at the theory of light in the classical world.

Light is a form of energy. It can be produced in various ways, transforming electrical energy (as seen, for example, in a light bulb or in the redness of toaster resistances) or chemical energy (as in candles and combustion processes in general). The sunlight, a consequence of the high temperatures present on our star's surface, comes from nuclear fusion processes that take place inside it. Also, the radioactive particles produced by a nuclear reactor here on Earth emit a blue light when they enter the water (which ionize, i.e., tear electrons from atoms).

It only takes a small amount of energy put into any substance to heat it. At small scales, this can be felt like a moderate temperature increase (as those who dabble with DIY on weekends know, nails get warm after a series of hammering or if they are torn from the wood with pliers). If we supply enough energy to a piece of iron, it emits light radiation; initially, it is reddish in color. Then, as the temperature increases, we see orange, yellow, green, and blue tones appear in order. In the end, if the heat is high enough, the emitted light becomes white, resulting from the sum of all colors.

However, most of the bodies around us are visible not because they emit light but because they reflect it. Excluding the case of mirrors, the reflection is always imperfect, not total: A red object appears to us as such because it reflects only this component of the light and absorbs orange, green, violet, and so on. The pigments of paints are chemical substances that have the property of accurately reflecting specific colors with a selective mechanism. White objects, alternatively, reflect all the components of light, while black ones absorb them all: therefore, the dark asphalt of a parking lot becomes hot on summer days, and this is the reason why, in the tropics, it is better to dress in light-colored clothing. These phenomena of absorption, reflection, and heating, concerning the various colors, have properties that can be measured and quantified by various scientific instruments.

Light is full of oddities. Here you are; we see you because the light rays reflected from your body affect our eyes. How interesting! Our mutual friend Edward is observing a painting instead: the rays of the you-us interaction (normally invisible, except when we are in a dusty or smoky room) intersect with those of the Edward-paint interaction without any apparent interference. But if we concentrate on an object, the beams produced by two flashlights, we realize that the intensity of the lighting doubles, so there is an interaction between the light rays.

Let us now examine a goldfish tank. First, we turn off the light in the room and turn on a flashlight. Then, helping ourselves with some dust suspended in the air, maybe produced by banging two blackboard erasers or a dust rag, we see that the light rays bend when they hit the water (and that the poor little fish is looking at us perplexed, hopefully waiting for some food). This phenomenon whereby transparent substances such as glass deflect light is called refraction.

When the Boy Scouts light a fire by concentrating the sun's rays on a little dry wood through a lens, they are taking advantage of this property: The lenses bend all the light rays, making them concentrate at a point called 'fire,' and this increases the amount of energy until it is so high that it triggers the combustion.

A glass prism can decompose the light into its components, the so-called 'spectrum.' These correspond to the colors of the rainbow: red, orange, yellow, green, blue, indigo, and violet (to memorize the order remember the initials ROYGBIV). Our eyes react to this type of light, called 'visible,' but we know that there are also invisible types. On one side of the spectrum, there is the so-called 'infrared' long wave range (of this type, for example, is the radiation produced by certain heaters, the toaster resistances, or the embers of a dying fire). On the other side, there are the 'ultraviolet' rays, short wave (an example is the radiation emitted by an arc welding machine, and that is why those who use it must wear protective glasses).

Therefore, the white light is a mixture of various colors in equal parts. With special instruments, we can quantify the characteristics of each color band, more properly, their wavelength, and report the results on a graph. We find that the graph assumes a bell shape whose peak is at a particular wavelength. At low temperatures, the peak corresponds to long waves, i.e., red light. Increasing the heat, the curve's maximum moves to the right, where the short waves are, i.e., violet light. Still, up to certain temperature values, the number of other colors is sufficient to ensure that the emitted light remains white. After these thresholds, the objects emit a blue glow.

If you look at the sky on a clear night, you will notice that the stars shine with slightly different colors: Those tending to be reddish are colder than white ones, which in turn are colder than blue ones. These gradations correspond to varying stages of evolution in the life of the stars as they consume their nuclear fuel. This simple identity card of light was the starting point of quantum theory, as we will see in more detail in a little while.

2.2 How Fast Does Light Travel?

Before approaching quantum physics and wave theory, there is another concept that we have to discuss first.

Light is an entity that 'travels' in space, for example, from a light bulb to our retina. This concept is not entirely intuitive. In the eyes of a child, light is something that shines, not that moves, but that's just the way it is. Galileo was one of the first to try to measure its speed, with the help of two assistants placed on top of two nearby hills who spent the night covering and uncovering two lanterns at predetermined times. When they saw the other light, they had to communicate it aloud to an external observer (Galileo himself), who made his measurements by moving at various distances from the two sources. This experiment is an excellent way to measure the speed of sound, according to the same principle that a certain amount of time elapses between seeing lightning and hearing thunder. The sound is not very fast; it goes at about 343m/s, so the effect is perceivable to the naked eye. For example, it takes three seconds before the thunderbolt comes from a lightning bolt that falls one kilometer away. But Galileo's simple experiment was not suitable to measure the speed of light, which is enormously higher.

In 1676, a Danish astronomer named Ole Römer, who at the time worked at the Paris Observatory, pointed his telescope towards the then-known Jupiter satellites (called 'Galileans' or 'Medici' because they were discovered by the usual Galileo less than a century earlier and dedicated by him to Cosimo de Medici). He focused on their eclipses and noticed a delay with which the moons disappeared and reappeared behind the big planet; this small-time interval depended mysteriously on the distance between Earth and Jupiter, which changes during the year (for example, Ganymede seemed to be early in December and late in July). Römer understood that the effect was due to the finite speed of light, according to a principle similar to that of the delay between thunder and lightning.

In 1685, the first reliable data on the distance between the two planets became available, which, combined with Römer's precise observations, allowed us to calculate the speed of light: It resulted in an impressive value of 300,000 km/s, immensely greater than that of sound. In 1850, Armand Fizeau and Jean Foucault, two skilled French experimenters in fierce competition, were the first to calculate this speed with direct methods on Earth without resorting to astronomical measurements. It was the beginning of a chase race between various scientists searching for the most precise value possible, which continues to this day. The most accredited today, which in physics is indicated by the letter c, is equal to 2,997,924,58 meters per second (186,000 miles per second). We observe incidentally that this c is the same that appears in the famous formula E=mc2. We will find it several times because it is one of the main pieces of that great puzzle called the universe changed.

2.3 Wave Theory and Electromagnetic Theory

Earlier, we discussed the subject of light from the point of view of classical physics; it is now time to introduce light from a different perspective.

We can start our journey in quantum physics with Robert Hooke, an English scientist, architect, and polymath who lived between the 17th and 18th centuries.

Using a microscope, Mr. Hooke was the first to visualize a microorganism.

He also wrote the famous book *Micrographia* (1665) and, trying to explain the origin of colors, developed his "pulse theory."

In *Micrographia*, he had noted the colored rings in thin transparent films and interpreted them in terms of vibrating pulses of light. He also speculated that the vibrations were transverse to the direction of propagation and that the waves were like those generated by a stone dropped in water. Hooke's analysis of color was in the Aristotelian modificationist tradition: All colors were a modification of white light. In the case of thin films, the colors were a consequence of 'confusions' in the reflections and refractions of white light. Nonetheless, Hooke's pulse theory of light, and his belief in the universal nature of vibrations, is considered a precursor of wave theories.

Subsequently, Christiaan Huygens, a Dutch physicist, mathematician, and astronomer, developed a mathematical wave theory of light (1678) on a theory that was representing light as waves.

In his book, Treatise on light, Huygens proposed that light was emitted in all directions as a series of waves in a medium called *Luminiferous ether*. However, he and Newton could only envision light waves as longitudinal, propagating like sound and other mechanical waves. Also, since waves are not affected by gravity, he assumed that light slows down upon entering a denser medium.

Let's jump forward a century to introduce Thomas Young, a brilliant British polymath that made numerous contributions to the fields of light, vision, energy, solid mechanics, and Egyptology.

In Young's judgment, the most important was establishing the wave theory of light of his many achievements. Young worked openly in contrast with Newton's century-old view and, in his opera, Opticks, argued that light behaves like particles.

Young embraced the wave theory of light and developed various demonstrations to support this viewpoint.

The most famous of these demonstrations was Young's interference experiment, which is considered the predecessor of the double-slit experiment.

The double-slit experiment (illustrated in Fig.1) was one of the key ways physicists showed that light could behave like a wave. When you shoot rays of light through two slits, they interfere with each other like waves, creating a specific, predictable pattern on a screen placed behind the slits. This behavior of light is known as a diffraction pattern.

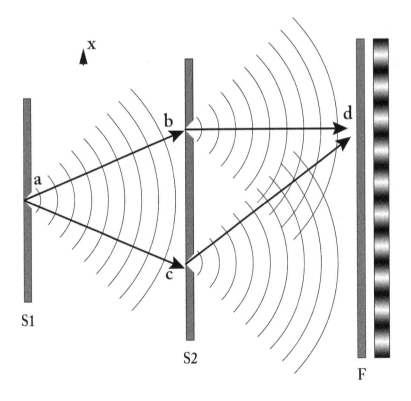

Fig.1 - The double-slit experiment

The light corpuscular theory (1637) states that light consists of small discrete particles that travel in a straight line with a finite velocity and possess impetus. However, this theory was in direct conflict with wave theory and was (temporarily) set aside.

In 1845, just 170 years ago, Faraday discovered that a magnetic field influenced polarized light. This phenomenon is known as the Faraday effect or the magneto-optical effect. Thanks to this discovery, scientists started to relate light with electromagnetism for the first time. The following year, in May 1846, Faraday published the article *Thoughts on Ray Vibrations*, in which he speculated that light could be a vibration of the electric and magnetic lines of force.

Michael Faraday, through his experiments, showed how a changing magnetic field induces an electromotive force (EMF), resulting in an electric current. He also found that electric fields sometimes act like magnetic fields and developed equations to calculate the forces exerted by both.

James Maxwell, a Scottish physicist, was one of the very few scientists who paid attention to Faraday's idea. It was a brave move for a young academic, but he felt that this was one of the missing pieces to understanding magnetism and the true nature of light. So, Maxwell started to work on a set of equations that held true for all electromagnetic interactions. In the process of developing his all-encompassing equations, Maxwell predicted the existence of electromagnetic waves.

Maxwell's first and second equations are a form of Gauss's Law, but the most interesting for us is Maxwell's third equation.

This last equation is based on Faraday's work. Starting from Faraday's law of induction, which says that a changing magnetic field will induce an electromotive force in a loop of wire, Maxwell developed a more general law that shows the value of that induced EMF.

Maxwell's third law states that the EMF is equal to the line integral of the electric field over a closed loop.

$$\int \vec{E} \cdot \vec{ds} = -\frac{d\Phi}{dt}$$

$\vec{E}$ = Electric field

$\vec{ds}$ = Infinitesimal element of closed loop

$d\Phi$ = Change in magnetic flux

dt = Change in time

This equation highlights the connection between a changing magnetic flux and an induced electric field.

On differentiating his partial differential equations, Maxwell obtained mathematical wave equations. Maxwell was then able to mathematically prove that electromagnetic signals are not transmitted instantaneously but are communicated through space as waves, but there is more!

He proved that these mathematical wireless electromagnetic waves traveled at the same speed as light. This prompted his characteristically modest understatement:

> [...] It seems we have strong reason to conclude that light itself (including radiant heat and other radiations, if any) is an electromagnetic disturbance in the form of waves propagated through the electromagnetic field according to electromagnetic laws (1865).

In one bold leap, he had united not simply electricity and magnetism but also light, heat, and "others radiations, if any."

This was incredible progress for the field at that time, but Maxwell didn't consider the *Ultraviolet catastrophe.*

2.4 Quantum Theory

One of the most important clues that light had to be more than just a wave was what is known as the *ultraviolet catastrophe.*

This name might seem like an exaggeration, but the *ultraviolet catastrophe* was disastrous for the conventional thinking about the physics of light.

In the previous chapters, we talked about how objects radiate heat. Specifically, the amount of heat that an object emits over time is proportional to its temperature, but there is more than just heat.

Objects also radiate energy that covers a wide range of frequencies on the electromagnetic spectrum, basically all different kinds of light.

Let's now consider a blackbody, which Gustav R. Kirchhoff first defined in 1859 as an object that absorbs all radiation falling upon it, without reflecting any, and radiates energy accordingly. Such a conception of an ideal blackbody was crucial for understanding heat radiation and its laws. Since a complete blackbody does not exist in nature, it had to be constructed.

It is possible to predict the intensity of the energy coming from a blackbody (blackbody radiation) based on its temperature.

When the physicists developed an equation to evaluate this intensity, starting from the assumption that light is a wave, they found the limits of this theory.

The equation used, known as Rayleigh-Jeans law, predicted that the higher the frequency of the radiation, the higher the intensity, and that matched with experimental results well, but only up to a certain point.

Once the frequency of light reached the ultraviolet range (or even higher), the Rayleigh-Jeans law showed its limits, not fitting the results of the experiments at all.

The Rayleigh-Jeans law agrees with experimental results at large wavelengths (low frequencies) but strongly disagrees at short (high frequencies) wavelengths. This inconsistency between observations and the predictions of classical physics is commonly known as the *ultraviolet catastrophe.*

As per the results of the experiments—at a particular frequency, the light would be at its most intense. However, after that, the intensity would drop as the frequency increased.

The warmer the object, the higher the frequency of the peak intensity, but there was always a peak. According to wave theory, it wasn't supposed to be this way!

Even worse, summing up all the contributions of higher and higher frequencies to calculate the total power emitted by a blackbody, the Rayleigh-Jeans law predicted that we would reach infinite power, which directly contradicts the *conservation of energy principle.*

The *ultraviolet catastrophe* highlighted that something was wrong with physicists' thinking about light.

The catastrophe was resolved in 1900 using an equation derived by German physicists Max Plank. This equation gave the correct radiation at all frequencies and was a foundational aspect of the development of quantum mechanics in the early 20th century.

We can say that *Planck's radiation law* is a mathematical equation that describes the distribution of energy that reflects the energies of blackbody radiation (see Fig.2).

Planck's law is actually very simple, but the concept was based on something entirely new at that time. According to Planck, electromagnetic energy takes the form of tiny, discrete packets called *quanta*. This might not sound intuitive, but the main idea is that you can't divide energy into anything smaller than these quanta packets after a certain point.

The energy (E) of each quantum is equal to the frequency of the light (f) times a tiny number called Planck's constant (h), which I'll explain more in detail later.

Using Planck's radiation law to predict the intensity of a blackbody allowed physicists to predict the experimental results perfectly, including those peak intensities.

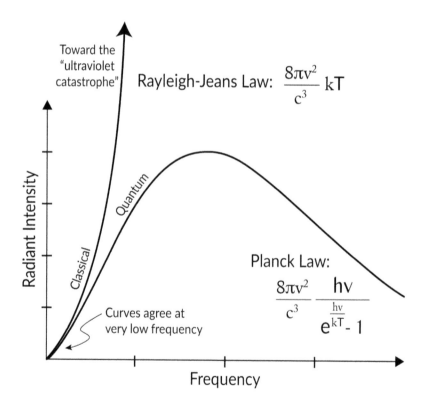

Fig.2 - *Ultraviolet catastrophe vs Planck Law*

Ok, but how did Planck manage to solve the ultraviolet catastrophe?

Planck assumed that the origin of the radiation is atoms in an oscillation state and that the vibrational energy of each oscillator can take only discrete values. Also, Planck thought that when the oscillator switched from a higher state of energy (E1) to a lower state of energy (E2), the amount of differential energy (E1 - E2) or the amount of quantum radiation was equal to the product of frequency (v) and Planck's constant (h), previously introduced: $E_1 - E_2 = hv$.

In this book, we will not go into the details of how Planck determined this constant or the mathematical demonstration to derive the formula.

Planck's law for the energy $E\lambda$ radiated per unit volume by a cavity of a blackbody in the wavelength interval λ to $\lambda + \Delta\lambda$ ($\Delta\lambda$ denotes an increment of wavelength) can be written as:

$$E_\lambda = \frac{8\pi hc}{\lambda^5} \times \frac{1}{\exp(hc/kT\lambda) - 1}$$

h = **Planck's constant**

c = **Speed of light**

k = **Boltzmann constant**

T = **Absolute temperature**

The wavelength of the emitted radiation is inversely proportional to its frequency, or $\lambda = c/v$. The value of Planck's constant is defined as $6.62607015 \times 10^{-34}$ Js (joule·second). Explaining how Planck determined this constant requires a mathematical demonstration to drive the formula, which would be too advanced for this book. Let's just say that he was able to compute them based on blackbody radiation data.

Planck's formula demonstrates that, in the case of the blackbody, with a temperature of several hundred degrees, we can see in the electromagnetic spectrum that most radiation is infrared if the blackbody reaches higher temperatures, the total energy released increases, and the emitted spectrum shifts towards shorter wavelengths. This means that at higher temperatures, a blackbody radiates primarily visible light.

2.5 Photoelectric Effect

Solving the ultraviolet catastrophe, Planck opened new opportunities to rethink physics as it was always conceived.

Before Plank's theories, energy was regarded as a continuous flow. Still, now the concept that energy could only exist in discrete packets (quanta) was exciting and scary at the same time.

Einstein played a significant role in reworking physics using this new information, and he won a Nobel prize for it in 1925.

In 1905, Einstein argued that light energy traveled in packets, called photons, which would make light behave like a particle. This was in direct contract with the multitude of experiments showing that light behaved like a wave.

To prove the theory that light traveled in discrete packets, Einstein devised an experiment using the photoelectric effect.

This effect consists of irradiating a metallic surface with light and observing the electrons emitted by the surface.

Basically, when you shine a beam of light on a metal plate, electrons leave the plate and hit a nearby collector, creating a current. Einstein realized that by studying the way the electrons left the plate, physicists could learn a lot about the properties of light.

The kinetic energy of the emitted electrons depends on the frequency v of the radiation. Also, there is a threshold frequency vo below which no electrons are emitted for a given metal. Therefore, the emission takes place as soon as the beam of light shines on the surface, without any delay.

It is essential to observe that both the particle theory and the wave theory of light predict that light knocks electrons out of the metal plate, but they put forward different reasons for why this happens.

According to wave theory, when a beam of light hits an electron, the force exerted knocks the electron out of the metal. Increasing the light intensity will increase the power of the electric field that is exerting a force on the electrons. As a result, more electrons are ejected from the metal plate with a higher speed and higher kinetic energy.

It is important to note that, according to wave theory, the frequency of light should not make any difference.

According to particle theory, electrons get ejected from the metal plate since individual photons hit them. When the collision happens, the photon is destroyed, and its energy is transferred to the electron, which is knocked out of the metal. A minimum amount of energy is required for this effect to happen since the electron is normally attracted to the metal.

Basically, an atom in the metal can absorb either a whole photon or nothing.

Part of the energy absorbed is used to tear the electron away from the metal, while the rest is converted into the kinetic energy of the emitted electron (see Fig.3).

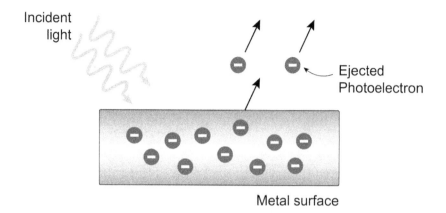

Fig.3 - Photoelectric effect

To release, the electron requires a fixed amount of energy (W), known as the metal's work function. The electron won't go anywhere if the photon has less energy than the work function.

According to particle theory, we can say that the energy of the photon is equal to the work function, W, plus the maximum kinetic energy:

$$E = KE_{max}$$

The energy of the photon is also equal to Planck's constant times the frequency, which means:

$$hf = W + KE_{max}$$

According to the equation above, we can see a direct correlation between the frequency of light and the maximum kinetic energy.

If we increase the frequency, the maximum kinetic energy should increase accordingly.

Also, going below a certain frequency, where Planck's constant time-frequency is equal to the work function, will not eject any electrons.

$$hf = W$$

We can conclude that increasing the intensity of the beam of light will increase the number of electrons knocked off the metal plate, but it won't affect their maximum kinetic energy.

So, which one is correct, particle theory or wave theory?

Before we know the answer, we need to ask ourselves a few simple questions, as Einstein did. Is there a frequency below which electrons are not ejected from the metal? Yes, and below that frequency, no electrons are emitted.

What happens if you raise the frequency? The higher the frequency is, the higher the maximum kinetic energy of the electrons.

Does the intensity of the light affect the maximum kinetic energy of the electrons? Increasing the intensity of the light only affects the number of electrons ejected and does not affect the maximum kinetic energy.

Based on this evidence, Einstein concluded that photons really exist, and the light travels in discrete packets and behaves like a particle.

2.6 Compton Effect

In 1923 Arthur Holly Compton demonstrated with another experiment the particle nature of electromagnetic radiation, and for this reason, he won the Nobel prize in 1927. It was a sensational discovery at the time: The wave nature of light had been well-demonstrated, but the idea that light had both wave and particle properties was not easily accepted.

Einstein had proposed light quanta in 1905 to explain the photoelectric effect, but Compton did not build on Einstein's work.

The *Compton effect* showed that the wavelength shift seen when low intensity X-rays scattered from electrons could be explained by a particle theory of X-rays but not a wave theory.

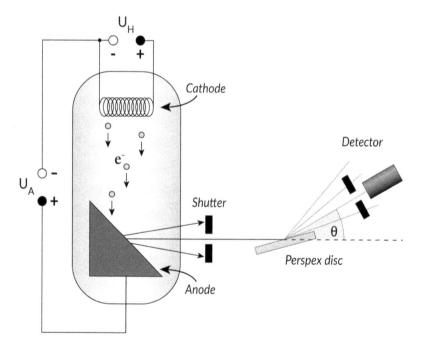

Fig.4 - Compton effect, original setup

To prove that Compton applied X-rays to crystals, he devised an experiment consisting of an X-ray tube with a molybdenum anode, a Perspex disc, and an X-ray detector mounted rotatable around the disk (see Fig.4).

In the X-ray tube, free electrons are generated in the proximity of the cathode; they are accelerated and hit the inclined molybdenum anode. Then, the photons of the X-rays hit the Perspex disc at a certain wavelength range and are scattered. The X-ray detector measures the resulting energy spectrum. Since the X-ray detector can move, the device is manually rotated to take measurements of the energy spectrum at different angles.

The scattering angles measured are typically 0 degrees, 60 degrees, and 120 degrees. Through this measurement process, the energy of photons during the scattering process changes depending on the scattering angle.

The effect can easily be explained in the particle theory world. The electrons can be assumed to be at rest before the scattering. If the photon collides with the electron, it transfers a part of its energy, and the electron receives kinetic energy, as observed in the *photoelectric effect* experiment. Compton was then able to derive the mathematical relationship between the shift in wavelength and the scattering angle of the X-rays by assuming that each scattered X-ray photon interacted with only one electron.

$$\lambda' - \lambda = \frac{h}{m_e c} (1 - \cos \theta)$$

λ = Initial wavelenght
λ' = Wavelenght after scattering
h = Planck's constant
m_e = Electron mass
c = Speed of light
θ = Scattering angle

The Compton effect can only be explained in the particle picture of quantum theory but not in the wave picture. Therefore, this effect is a critical experiment in quantum theory. Moreover, the experiment was the first proof, after the photoelectric effect, of the particle behavior of radiation.

Compton's experiment convinced physicists that light could be treated as a stream of particle-like objects (quanta called photons), whose energy is proportional to the light wave's frequency.

2.7 The Wave-Particle Duality Dilemma

Through Einstein's photoelectric effect experiment and Compton experiment, we discovered that light behaves like particles, but there is one thing we didn't consider; what about all those experiments that showed light behaving like a wave? Can we simply dismiss them?

No, the thing is that light can behave like both. Depending on the circumstance, it can act like a particle or a wave, this is called *wave-particle duality.*

Light waves have both a wavelength, the distance from tip to tip, and a frequency, which is the number of waves that pass by a point per unit of time (see Fig. 5).

The two are inversely proportional since the shorter the wave, the more of them can go by per second, resulting in a higher frequency.

The electromagnetic spectrum shows light of all the different wavelengths, from gamma rays to radio waves, including a tiny area in the middle of the spectrum, which is the visible light.

Wave theory of light could not explain the photoelectric effect. As we have seen in the previous chapters, the ability of light to eject an electron depends only on its frequency and not its

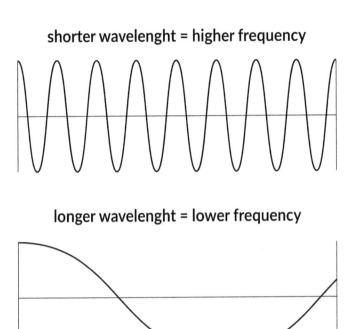

shorter wavelenght = higher frequency

longer wavelenght = lower frequency

x = wavelenght   v = frequency

Fig.5 - Shorter versus longer wavelength

intensity. If the beam of light that hits a metallic plate is below a certain frequency, even a very intense beam could not eject an electron. Above a certain frequency, the faintest beam possible will eject electrons.

This leads us to Planck's theory that we have previously discussed. Planck claimed that energy is not continuous; it is quantized, which means that all energies are multiples of the smallest fundamental unit of energy (Planck's energy).

Quantum theory shows that everything is quantized, including space and time. Basically, you can't infinitely subdivide space and time; you will eventually reach a point where they cannot be divided further.

Einstein rationalized that light must also be made of quanta or, more precisely, of particles of light called photons. This explains the photoelectric effect, considering that it requires even only a single photon, charged with the minimum amount of energy needed, to eject an electron.

But knowing this doesn't allow us to invalidate all the experiments that proved that light behaves like a wave.

We must accept that light obeys wave-particle duality, which means it is both a particle and a wave.

We must understand that when it comes to the physics of infinitely small objects, our intuitive understanding of the world and the principles governing its functioning just don't apply.

It is impossible to describe light using concepts we are familiar with and work on a bigger scale. Working with small particles is something outside the way we have directly experienced the world; that's why our intuition doesn't work well. Newton's laws were reigning supreme in classical physics, but in the world of the very small, that's not the case.

The discovery of Planck's law and the idea that energy travels in discrete packets (quanta) became the foundation for the concepts and equations used to analyze the behavior of infinitely small objects. This was the first of a series of discoveries that brought the *quantum revolution*, entirely changing the landscape of physics and how we observe the universe.

~ Part 3 ~
You Can't Know Everything

3.1 How Wave-Particle Duality Applies to the Matter

Around 1924, Louis Victor de-Broglie proposed the idea that wave-particle duality doesn't only apply to light; it can apply to basically everything.

Applying wave-particle duality to matter led to a new way to analyze the behavior of particles with an accuracy never seen before. This also helped to understand that there are some characteristics of the physics of infinitely small objects that we will never be able to describe accurately.

Symmetry surrounds us; animals, plants, people, and everything around us shows some symmetrical properties. Symmetry creates harmony and balance, but it had a more practical effect in De Broglie's case.

De Broglie theorized that if the light behaves both like a wave and a particle, then due to the inherent symmetry of nature, we could expect to find the same behavior in matter.

Mathematics seemed to support him in this theory:

$$p = \frac{h}{\lambda}$$

$p = $ **Momentum**

$h = $ **Planck's constant**

$\lambda = $ **Wavelenght**

According to De Broglie's theory, light's momentum equation would also apply to the matter.

This means that it is possible to find the wavelength of any particle of matter if the momentum is known.

To test his theory, De Broglie relied on another experiment with electrons, similar to the double-slit experiment used by scientists to prove that light behaves like a wave.

To see if matter behaves like a wave, physicists used a variation of the double-slit experiment; instead of light, they used a beam of electrons.

In this specific experiment, the beam of electrons is shot at a plate with two slits cut into it.

Behind the plate, a screen glowed wherever an electron hit it. Scientists noticed that electrons, like light, created a diffraction pattern.

This behavior implied that the electrons were acting like waves. Also, the experiment showed the interference effect of a single electron with the field of many electrons. (see Fig.6).

The experiment showed that De Broglie was right—electrons behave like waves and particles, which is valid for everything around us.

An arrow in the air has a corresponding wavelength; your bicycle has a wavelength; even people's bodies can have a wavelength!

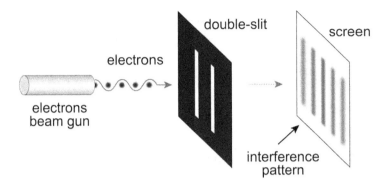

electrons beam gun

electrons

double-slit

screen

interference pattern

Fig.6 - A variation of double-slit experiment that uses a beam of electrons.

This idea might seem counterintuitive, but most quantum concepts mechanics are. Many people might ask why, if everything has a wavelength, we cannot see them?

Mathematics, in this case, comes to our aid; according to light's momentum equation, the wavelength is equal to Planck's constant divided by the momentum.

$$\lambda = \frac{h}{p}$$

λ = **Wavelenght**

h = **Planck's constant**

p = **Momentum**

As you might remember, Planck's constant (6.63×10^{-34} Js) is a very tiny number and, according to the equation above, the larger the momentum, the smaller the wavelength.

Basically, for any object that is big enough to see with the naked eye, the wavelength is so small that we cannot detect it without proper instruments.

Take, as an example, a ball with a mass of 0.2kg flying through the air at 45 meters per second.

To find the ball's wavelength, we divide Planck's constant by the ball's mass times its velocity.

Without even going through the calculation, we can rightly predict that the wavelength would be incredibly small!

There are no ways yet to measure waves so tiny, and for this reason, it is impossible to see that our ball is also a wave.

3.2 Schrödinger's Quantum Theory and Unified Field Theory

As discussed in the previous chapter, quantum mechanics are strongly related to the wave properties of matter, but it also involves probability.

Let's look another time at the double-slit experiment with electrons. In an initial observation, it might seem that the electrons going through the slits are landing on the screen in random areas. That's not the case. If we keep observing for a more extended period, we can see a diffraction pattern.

If we continue to observe, it will soon be evident that a high number of electrons land in the spots corresponding to the bright bands in the pattern. This happens because probability plays a considerable role in how electrons and matter behave on the quantum level.

In the 1910s, Schrödinger became acquainted with the works of Planck, Einstein, and others but wasn't terribly interested in giving up classical physics just yet. That all changed when he developed tuberculosis and spent some time in and out of sanatoriums regaining his health. While convalescing, the scientist started to warm up to the ideas, especially quantum theory. He was fascinated with the possibility that the electromagnetic spectrum could have differing effects on a wide variety of elements and wanted to discover if he could find a universal way to predict the behavior of electrons.

Schrödinger played around with these thoughts and concluded that the only way to do this would be to predict the nature of radiation itself. While he couldn't find a way to do this, the articles he published proposing these concepts opened the door for a new brand of theoretical physics. Also, they led to a few concrete advancements, such as wave mechanics and an interesting new atomic model, which we'll get into shortly. Schrödinger's other contribution to theoretical physics was his attempt to create a unified field theory, which is sort of the Holy Grail of quantum physics. A *unified field theory* (or UFT) was attempted by Einstein when he was working on his theory of relativity and is still a matter of great debate among quantum scientists.

A unified field theory would bring together all the fundamental interactions and relationships in quantum physics under one set of proven laws. This would mean that scholars would be able to predict the behavior of all matter based on mathematical proofs and observable actions with no deviations. The matter would behave according to these laws, and we'd be able to connect the dots between interactions, electromagnetic fields and waves, particles, and spacetime. There have been more than a few efforts to write and prove a unified field theory for quantum physics (classical physics has one), but no one is yet to succeed. One such popular attempt is called "the theory of everything," Let's face it, that sounds a bit pretentious.

One thing Schrödinger succeeded in doing was becoming the father of wave mechanics. His theories on the behaviors of particle waves gave birth to this new sub-discipline in the mid-1920s. The basis of his theories was rooted in the premise of the behavior of a hydrogen atom in a system independent of time constraints. Schrödinger wanted to know what would happen if time was taken out of the equation when predicting the wave-particle behavior of the atom. In the resulting rapid-fire series of four papers, the physicist laid out his predictions and gave the world the first look at his now-famous equation; the second paper edited the equation to account for harmonics within the system.

The third and fourth papers in the series were devoted to showing the world how to compare his equation to work involved in the uncertainty principle and taught his colleagues how to plug in the correct complex numbers directly into his equation to avoid calculating so many derivatives. This series of papers is still considered one of modern science's most significant scientific accomplishments. It paved the way for physicists to begin studying wave behavior in a much more controlled and accurate manner.

It also marked the beginning of some seriously complicated math, and many believe Schrödinger's equation to be the cut-off between classical and quantum physics.

Do you see now why it's so difficult to pinpoint one defining moment? Even Schrödinger himself wasn't thrilled with what he'd done once it was over and published. He recognized that he had caused a giant rift between classical physics and the new quantum discipline. As someone who loved the principles of classical physics, he never wanted to be as correct as he was, but once his research was published, there was no going back.

What exactly was so special about Schrödinger's equation, other than the fancy numbers? And why did it have such a profound effect on quantum physics? To begin with, it is a partial linear differential equation, which means it has a lot of moving parts to get to its solution. Heck, that's a lot of words just to describe an equation. In classical physics, there is Newton's second law of motion, which you may recall is shown mathematically as F=ma or force equals mass times acceleration. It predicts the movement of an object as it speeds up, proportional to its mass. Think of Schrödinger's equation as the quantum physics counterpart to Newton's second law. Yes, it was that groundbreaking and that important. Below here, you will see the equation:

$$\frac{ih}{2\pi}\frac{\partial \Psi}{\partial t} = -\frac{h^2}{8\pi^2 m}\left(\frac{\partial^2 \Psi}{\partial x^2} + \frac{\partial^2 \Psi}{\partial y^2} + \frac{\partial^2 \Psi}{\partial z^2}\right) + V\Psi$$

Yeah, we know. This is a lot to unpack, so we're just going to pay the baggage fees on this one and send it on its way. After all, this is a book for beginners. This sucker took F=ma and turned it on its classical physics head.

When quantum mechanics looks at the wave nature of matter, it is mainly concerned with the probability that particles, like electrons, will be in certain places at certain times. One of the main reasons the equation is helpful is that you can use it to predict the probability of finding a particle at any given point in space; this is known as *the probability density function.*

Schrödinger was also intrigued by the thought of updating the atomic model to account for the wave behavior of electrons as they orbited the nucleus. After careful analysis, the scientist created the first truly three-dimensional, accurate model of the atom, using his wave mechanics theory and equation. Schrödinger's model of the atom includes an electron cloud, moving in and out around the nucleus in a wave pattern. Using this model, scientists can predict where the electrons might be at any given time. This differed from the earlier Bohr model that showed the electrons in a set and layered orbits that did not fluctuate due to wave-particle duality.

You can see now why Schrödinger's theories are regarded as groundbreaking; it's said that with this one calculation, Schrödinger flung open the door of quantum mechanics, and it was never able to be shut again.

3.3 Yes, Yes, the Cat...

Early in his career, Schrödinger was interested in sticking to classical physics, and as he aged, he leaped into quantum physics and theoretical physics. He was an outlier among his colleagues for waiting so long to join the game and being sad for himself that he did (despite the accolades and the Nobel Prize), but he was also a certified odd bird. He had a very untraditional marital arrangement, marked publicly by emigrating to Ireland with his wife, his mistress, and the children he fathered with both women. He wrote a premise on genetics, which inspired a whole generation of geneticists and led to the discovery of the human genome. Schrödinger also authored a treatise on the nature of colors in the visible light spectrum and color perception in humans. He had a lifelong curiosity for the intersection of science and philosophy.

His most famous thought experiment is that which is known as Schrödinger's cat. In this exercise, Schrödinger theorized that a cat locked inside a box with a deadly poison could be both alive and dead simultaneously. Yes, it's a paradox, and it was designed to be. Without opening the box and looking at it, one cannot tell the cat's state. But what if opening the box changes the predicted outcome? Schrödinger first introduced the paradox in a series of debates he held with Einstein. The thought experiment was his quiet way of railing back against certain interpretations of his quantum mechanics theories.

Schrödinger wasn't happy with the so-called Copenhagen Interpretation of his wave mechanics. This school of thought, led by Niels Bohr of atomic model fame, stated that wave function would collapse because there was no way to observe the nature of waves without interfering with them and causing disastrous results. Bohr and his colleagues were convinced that every act of measurement would affect the experiment until the outcomes were invalid. Schrödinger argued that no collapse had ever been physically observed, so how could Bohr prove his interpretation? Out of this frustration, Schrödinger's cat thought experiment was born. He wanted to show his fellow scientists that they were being ridiculous to think that, yes, while the observer effect is a thing, the mere act of looking at something would cause a drastic impact on its status. To do so, he put an imaginary cat in a box and began asking people if they thought it was alive or dead.

While this does seem a little ridiculous, it had a profound effect on the scientific community and the future of quantum physics. From Schrödinger's cat came the theory of quantum entanglement. Schrödinger himself was forced to concede that maybe his quantum wave mechanics couldn't explain everything all the time. He began to recognize that maybe what his Copenhagen-interpreting friends were seeing wasn't the breakdown of the wave function but the tangling up of waves as they crossed each other. Like children playing cat's cradle and getting their yarn hopelessly knotted up, maybe electrons were getting their waves tied up together, making their paths indistinguishable. The theory of quantum entanglement brought a new aspect to wave mechanics and made it possible for scientists to know what to look for when studying the behavior of subatomic particles.

Erwin Schrödinger died of tuberculosis in 1961 and was laid to rest in his native Austria. His wave equation is engraved above his tomb, and his wife was buried with him after her death in 1965. There was no word on what happened to the mistress. For what it's worth, Schrödinger always marched to his own drum. He joined the fray of quantum physics when it suited him, lending his brilliant insight and then bowing out to pursue his other passions whenever he pleased. He didn't give a hoot about the Nazis invading his homeland, and he told them so. He flaunted his open marriage in public in the 1930s and 40s, and he gave the world a scientific way to talk about dead cats. In one of his last public appearances in the 1950s, he even declined to talk about nuclear power, as he'd been asked, and spoke on philosophy at length until his audience protested. Schrödinger was fabulously gifted, delightfully weird, and tremendously impactful on the world of quantum physics.

3.4 Quantum Superposition

Physicists think that an electron position is not defined until you start to observe it. We can consider an electron in a set of different places at once, even if it is still just one electron.

Once the electron is measured or observed, it is only in one position. Somehow, measuring (or observing) forces the electron to be in a specific place.

We briefly encountered this concept in the previous chapter when discussing Schrödinger's atom model; I have mentioned the electron clouds moving in and out around the nucleus in a wave pattern.

This counterintuitive idea that a particle can assume more than one state simultaneously is called *quantum superposition*. The principle was described in *The Principles of Quantum Mechanics* (1947) by Paul Dirac as follows:

> The general principle of superposition of quantum mechanics applies to the states [that are theoretically possible without mutual interference or contradiction] ... of any dynamical system. It requires us to assume that between these states, there exists a peculiar relationship such that whenever the system is definitely in one state, we can consider it as being partly in each of two or more other states. The original state must be regarded as the result of a kind of superposition of the two or more new states in a way that cannot be conceived on classical ideas. Any state may be considered as the result of a superposition of two or more other states, and indeed in an infinite number of ways. Conversely, any two or more

states may be superposed to give a new state [...]The non-classical nature of the superposition process is brought out clearly if we consider the superposition of two states, A and B, such that there exists an observation which, when made on the system in state A, is certain to lead to one particular result, a say, and when made on the system in state B is certain to lead to some different result, b say. What will be the result of the observation when made on the system in the superposed state? The answer is that the result will be sometimes a and sometimes b, according to a probability law that depends on the relative weights of A and B in the superposition process. It will never be different from both a and b [i.e., either a or b]. The intermediate character of the state formed by superposition thus expresses itself through the probability of a particular result for an observation being intermediate between the corresponding probabilities for the original states, not through the result itself being intermediate between the corresponding results for the original states, (1947).

Schrödinger, with his famous thought experiment with the cat, was trying to explore this concept, using an example that is easier for the human mind to understand.

Quantum superposition is a fundamental principle of quantum mechanics. It states that, much like waves in classical physics, any two (or more) quantum states can be added together ('superposed'), resulting in another valid quantum state; conversely, every quantum state can be represented as a sum of two or more other distinct states. Mathematically, it refers to a property of solutions to the Schrödinger equation; since the Schrödinger equation is linear, any linear combination of solutions will also be a solution.

The effect of quantum superposition is one of the concepts totally counter to how we experience the world. Still, it is also the same idea powering modern quantum computers.

We will see in the following chapters that classical information, encoded in everyday computers, is a string of zeros and ones; quantum information has the property that the states can exist in a superposition of 0 and 1. This allows us to explore a much richer set of states and potentially solve problems that a computer will never be able to solve.

3.5 Heisenberg Uncertainty Principle

In the previous chapter, I introduced the concept of quantum superposition. We have explored the counterintuitive idea that a particle can assume more than one state simultaneously and that observing an electron affects the particle forcing it to be in a specific place.

What we didn't consider is the fact that there is still an uncertainty component in the measurement; the Heisenberg uncertainty principle explains this.

This concept was formalized by the German physicist Werner Heisenberg in 1927, and it is also called the "uncertainty principle" or "indeterminacy principle."

The principle says that an object's position and velocity cannot be measured precisely simultaneously, even in theory. So the very concepts of exact position and exact velocity together, in fact, have no meaning in nature.

It doesn't matter how good our measuring instrument is; we can only measure the position and momentum of a particle up to a certain level of precision.

We could get a better measurement of our electron's position, but we will have to sacrifice the accuracy of the measured momentum. Likewise, we could significantly improve the measurement of the electron's momentum, but at the same time, we will have to sacrifice some knowledge of its position.

The reason it is impossible to obtain an accurate measurement of both position and momentum is due to the concept of wave-particle duality, which I have introduced in the previous chapters.

Earlier in this book, I presented the light's momentum equation. According to this formula, the wave's momentum equals Planck's constant divided by its wavelength.

$$p = \frac{h}{\lambda}$$

$p =$ **Momentum**
$h =$ **Planck's constant**
$\lambda =$ **Wavelenght**

Using the wave function to describe the electron we are observing as a wave, we will be able to measure its exact momentum without particular issues.

The uncertainty in the position measurement arises from the fact that using this equation, we are considering the electron as a wave. A wave doesn't have an exact position; since we are describing the electron in a way that allows us to measure its momentum, we lose the ability to measure its position.

If we try to describe the electron as a particle, we will be able to measure its position, but then we will encounter a similar problem. The equations involved in measuring the position wouldn't allow us to measure the electron's momentum.

Paul Davies, in *Introduction to Physics and Philosophy* (1962), helps us to realize that this problem is not due to the technological limitations of our instruments:

> At the heart of the quantum revolution is Heisenberg's uncertainty principle [...] roughly [...] all physical quantities [...] are subject to unpredictable fluctuations so that their

values are not precisely defined. [...] [e.g., we are] free to measure [position x and the momentum p of a quantum particle] to arbitrary precision, but they cannot possess precise values simultaneously. The spread, or uncertainty, in their values, denoted by Ax and Ap [...] are such that [their] product [...] cannot be less than [...] Planck's constant, numerically very small [...] so that quantum effects are generally only important in the atomic domain [...] not [...] in daily life. [...]This uncertainty is inherent in nature and not merely the result of technological limitations in measurement, (1962), n.p.

Quantum physicists try to make the best of both wave and particle worlds by describing electrons as *wave packets*.

A wave packet is a collection of waves bundled together. Schrödinger's equation calculates the various waves that represent a quantum mechanical system (i.e., the electron that we were trying to measure before). Summing all the waves together can give scientists an approximation of the electron's position at the expense of the electron's momentum accuracy.

This limits how precisely we can measure, in the same instant, the combination of momentum and position of an electron. The following equation represents this uncertainty:

$$\Delta x \cdot \Delta p \approx \frac{h}{4\Pi}$$

Δx = **Uncertainty in position**
Δp = **Uncertainty in momentum**
h = **Planck's constant**

In the "normal scale world," this uncertainty is negligible. Still, it can be a real problem when we work at the quantum level— losing precision in position or momentum forces scientists to work with statistical approximations. There is basically a "built-in" limit on how much we can learn about particle behavior.

Jeremy Bernstein (1990) brilliantly highlights the problem in Quantum Profiles:

> If quantum mechanics is right, there is no way to get around the uncertainty principle. The reason that the electron's probability wave spread so much after we confined it, Heisenberg would argue, is that its momentum became almost completely indeterminate. In a manner of speaking, it headed off in all directions, (1990), n.p.

Quantum mechanics sometimes is just weird!

~ Part 4 ~
Quantum Theories

4.1 What Is Quantum Field Theory

You might think that the ideas introduced in the previous chapters of this book are weird. However, these ideas are almost a hundred years old. Quantum mechanics has been tested countless times and proven genuine. Frontier Science has moved on and is exploring new areas.

I have previously introduced Schrödinger's equation, which is used to show why electrons have only certain levels of energies and positions while rotating around an atom. However, this equation is only a partial quantum theory since it doesn't consider Einstein's relativity, and it works under the assumption that a non-quantized electrical field surrounds a proton.

Unlike matter, which is composed of individual particles that cannot be subdivided, classical electrical fields vary smoothly instead of assuming only certain discrete values.

In late 1920, Paul Dirac, an English theoretical physicist who is regarded as one of the most significant physicists of the 20th century, started to work on quantum mechanics.

Dirac started the second quantization revolution; he successfully merged quantum mechanics and Einstein's theory of special relativity and, more notably, found a way to make a fully quantum theory.

It is not the purpose of this book to discuss the theory of special relativity; suffice it to say that the theory is composed of the following two postulates:

- The laws of physics are invariant in all inertial frames of reference.

- The speed of light in a vacuum is the same for all observers, regardless of the motion of the light source or observer.

Dirac, in his famous paper *The Quantum Theory of the Emission and Absorption of Radiation*, coined the name *quantum electrodynamics* (QED) and merged quantum mechanics and the theory of relativity, finding a quantum formulation of the electric field surrounding the proton.

The English theoretical physicists derived an equation for transferring the characteristic quantum phenomenon of discreteness of physical quantities from the quantum mechanical treatment of particles to a corresponding treatment of fields.

Dirac's equation is consistent with both the principles of quantum mechanics and the theory of special relativity; it also allowed, once generalized, to cover all the subatomic forces.

The strong nuclear force, the weak nuclear force, and electromagnetism forces are all examples of what we call a *quantum field theory* (QFT).

Here is the Dirac's equation in the original form:

$$\left(\beta mc^2 + c\sum_{n=1}^{3}\alpha_n p_n\right)\psi(x,t) = i\hbar\frac{\partial\psi(x,t)}{\partial t}$$

Where ψ = ψ(x, t) is the wave function for the electron of rest mass m with spacetime coordinates x, t. The p1, p2, and p3 are the components of the momentum operator in the Schrödinger equation. Also, c is the speed of light, and ħ is the reduced Planck constant.

In modern physics theory, we can picture all subatomic particles as beginning with a field; then, the particles we see are just localized vibrations in the field. According to QFT, fields are everywhere; particles are just localized vibrations that move in a field (see Fig.7).

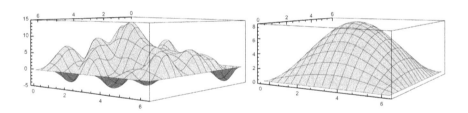

Fig.7 - Localized vibrations in quantum fields.

This concept is also able to explain how particles interact with each other. For example, let's take an electron. According to QFT, this particle is represented as vibration at a certain point of the electron field. However, suppose the electron we are observing emits a photon. In that case, the energy of the electron field sets up a localized vibration of a photon field that moves away from the original vibration.

The main concept I want you to absorb from this chapter is that fields for all known subatomic particles populate the ordinary space and that localized vibrations can be found everywhere. Furthermore, these fields can interact with each other, explaining how particles are created and destroyed; the energy of some vibrations moves from one field to another.

Calculating the behavior of these vibrations is not an easy task and requires advanced mathematical knowledge. Therefore, providing a solid demonstration of QFT is not within the scope of this book, and the information can be easily found in a more advanced book.

This chapter aims to help you understand that these vibrations are everywhere you look, even if we cannot see them, and help shape the world that we know.

4.2 The Standard Model of Particle Physics

Before introducing the *quantum and string theories*, it is worth spending a few paragraphs discussing the standard model of elementary particles.

The Standard Model of particle physics is the theory describing three of the four known fundamental forces in the universe (the electromagnetic, weak, and strong interactions, not including the gravitational force) and classifying all known elementary particles. It was developed in stages in the latter half of the 20th century, through the work of many scientists worldwide, with the current formulation being finalized in the mid-1970s upon experimental confirmation of the existence of quarks.

When we think of an atom, we generally think of a nucleus made of protons and neutrons, surrounded by a cloud of electrons. Each neutron and proton are built of smaller particles called quarks; these infinitely small objects build the universe as we know it.

Particles are categorized into matter particles (*fermions*) and force carrier particles (*gauge bosons*). In quantum field theory, force carriers, messenger particles, or intermediate particles are particles that give rise to forces between other particles.

Fermions are divided into *leptons* and *quarks*; of the latter, there are six types: *up, down, charm, strange, top,* and *bottom.*

There are six types of leptons as well, known as *flavors*, grouped in three generations. The first-generation leptons, also called *electronic leptons*, comprise the *electron* and the *electron neutrino*; the second is the *muonic leptons*, consisting of the *muon* and the *muon neutrino*; and the third is the *tauonic leptons*, comprising the *tau* and the *tau neutrino*.

Standard Model of Elementary Particles

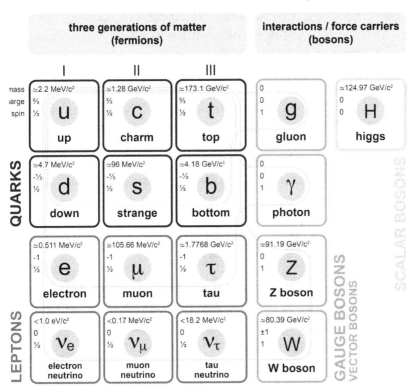

Fig.8 - Standard model of elementary particles.

The Standard Model of particle physics recognizes four kinds of *gauge bosons*: *photons*, which carry the electromagnetic interaction; *W* and *Z bosons*, which carry the weak interaction; and *gluons*, which carry the strong interaction (see Fig.8).

We know of four forces: *the strong nuclear force, the electromagnetic force, the weak nuclear force*, and *gravity*. We already encountered the electromagnetic force, and we all know what gravity is (in a classical sense); what about the other two?

The strong nuclear force holds most ordinary matter together because it confines quarks into particles such as the proton and neutron. Besides, the strong force binds these neutrons and protons to create atomic nuclei.

The weak nuclear force is the mechanism of interaction between subatomic particles that is responsible for the radioactive decay of atoms. The weak interaction participates in nuclear fission, and the theory describing its behavior and effects is sometimes called *electroweak theory* (EWT).

Gluons act as mediators of the strong nuclear force both inside the proton and between protons and neutrons. Photons are particles of light that carry the electromagnetic force.

W and Z bosons carry the weak nuclear force, which is involved in some forms of radioactivity and plays a role in how the sun burns.

The standard model also describes the Higgs field, which is a quantum field that permeates all of space. The Higgs boson is the local excitation of the Higgs field.

There is also one last (hypothetical) boson to talk about, the graviton, that will be introduced in the next chapter. Graviton is a particle that mediates the gravitational force, and it is definitely time to know more about it!

4.3 Quantum Gravity

There is a force that we didn't consider yet, the force that literally binds the universe together: gravity. You might find this strange, but gravity is incredibly weaker compared to the other forces like electromagnetism, strong nuclear force, and weak nuclear force.

The strong nuclear force is an attractive force between protons and neutrons that keep the nucleus together. *The weak nuclear* force is responsible for the radioactive decay of certain nuclei.

To give you an idea, gravity is 100.000.000.000.000.000. 000.000.000.000.000.000.000.000 (1×10^{41}) times weaker than the strong nuclear force. To put it in perspective, it is like comparing a particle to the size of the visible universe; it is a massive difference. Basically, since gravity is so weak in the quantum world, it cannot affect experiments at the particle scale; gravity does not exist for particles. To realize that gravity exists, we must work at a different level; it takes the mass of planets or stars to see this force in action.

In this chapter, I want to discuss the nature of this force in the quantum realm. Gravity, even if really weak, must apply in the micro-world and the best gravity theory we have is to be attributed to Einstein. *General relativity*, also known as the general theory of relativity, is the geometric theory of gravitation published by Albert Einstein in 1915 and is the current description of gravitation in modern physics. *General relativity* generalizes special relativity and refines Newton's law of universal gravitation, providing a unified description of gravity as a geometric property of space and time or four-dimensional spacetime.

The most obvious thing to do is apply general relativity to the subatomic realm.

Let's take, as an example, an electron orbiting a nucleus. According to Einstein's theory, the electron would progressively lose energy due to the gravity waves, reducing the distance from the proton until the two will collide. This doesn't seem to be a realistic behavior, but as happened with electromagnetism, it is about finding the quantum nature of gravity.

Various reasons lead us to think that gravity has a quantum nature:

- There are quantum theories for all the other forces; why not gravity?

- Einstein's general relativity is a classical theory, and, from the previous chapters, we know that classical theories don't really fit well in the quantum realm.

It seems reasonable to think that a theory of quantum gravity should exist, but on what elements can it be built?

We could start from the core principles that we know are true for all the other forces.

For instance, since the quantum theory of electromagnetism predicts the existence of photons, a similar theory applied to gravity will indicate the presence of gravitons.

There is no proof of gravitons' existence; that is why it is considered a speculative particle, but let's assume for a minute that they are real. Gravitons, if they exist, to align with Einstein's and Newton's theories of gravity, must have specific properties:

- The graviton must be massless to have gravity's infinite range.

- The graviton must be electrically neutral.

- The graviton must have a certain quantum spin, different from protons and electrons spin, to be an attractive force.

The problem is finding these particles; the gravity force in the quantum realm is so weak that it is currently impossible to create a graviton in a particle physics experiment. So instead, it has been tried to use particle accelerators, using electromagnetic fields to propel charged particles to very high speeds and energies and contain them in well-defined beams. Currently, the largest accelerator operating is the Large Hadron Collider (LHC) near Geneva, Switzerland, operated by the CERN. Other powerful accelerators are RHIC at Brookhaven National Laboratory in New York and, formerly, the Tevatron at Fermilab, Batavia, Illinois. Unfortunately, none of these incredibly expensive machines found a graviton yet.

There is a chance to find a graviton, but it is a very long shot; this possibility is based on the existence of additional dimensions beyond the familiar three. With new dimensions, we will have to reconsider the gravitational theory and possibly find gravitons with a completely different approach.

If we exclude the multidimensional option, a few quantum gravity theories were proposed that were moderately well received and theoretically possible. We can find superstring theory among them, which we will introduce in the next chapter.

A second idea is called *loop quantum gravity* (LQG). According to this theory, space-time is a network. The smooth background of Einstein's theory of gravity is replaced by nodes and links to which quantum properties are assigned. In this way, space is built up of discrete chunks.

The core idea is that there is the smallest quantum of space and time. Think about cutting a piece of paper. According to LQG, you can cut your paper until you reach a certain size; after that, it is impossible to make a smaller piece. Unfortunately, the physical dimensions assumed by LQG are too small to be tested in a laboratory. The best scientists can do is test some observable consequences of LQG theory. For this reason, so far, there is no evidence to confirm or disprove this idea.

There is still much work to be done before we get a solid theory. Still, assuming quantum gravity exists, it will have profound consequences regarding how we model the center of a black hole or the universe right before the Big Bang.

These two models have in common the idea that all the matter is concentrated in a single mathematical with zero sizes. These mass concentrations are called singularities and don't exist from the physical point of view. This does not mean that they are not real; it is just a sign that a theory has been pushed far beyond its limits to the point of falling apart.

It has not been proven that singularities do not exist, but quantum gravity becomes incredibly relevant when a high concentration of mass in a single point is created.

This means that it will be hard for us to understand the Big Bang or the center of a black hole until a theory that unites gravity and quantum mechanics is created.

We can say that understanding quantum gravity is a stepping stone to building a theory of everything.

4.4 String Theory

String theory proposes that rather than the elemental particles introduced in chapter 4.1, the smallest building blocks of the universe are tiny vibrating strings of energy, from which all the matter and all the known forces emanate. The general theory of relativity describes how gravity works, while quantum mechanics describes how strong nuclear force, weak nuclear force, and electromagnetic force work at a quantum scale. As I have previously mentioned, these two theories are not compatible. In general, relativity, space, and time are a smooth continuum, while quantum mechanics works with the idea that space and time can be represented with discrete quantities (quantized).

String theory is a popular attempt to resolve these incompatibilities and find a framework to explain how all the four known forces work. Unfortunately, the original formulation (bosonic string theory) had two main issues:

- Only bosons are taken into consideration, while fermions are ignored.

- It predicted the existence of a speculative faster than light particle (tachyon) that could break the time barrier and destabilize space.

When a string vibrates, the type of vibration determines which particle they look like on a larger scale. For the math to support string theories, more dimensions are required than the four we are used to (three for space and one for time). For instance, bosonic string theory works under the assumption that there are 27 different dimensions; the reason why we don't notice these extra dimensions is that they are curled up incredibly small. This extra-dimensional space is called *hyperspace*, and, according to string theory, it might allow us to explain quantum gravity. The reason why this might become possible is the fact that gravity, which describes the geometry of space-time itself, requires precise measurements of distance. Due to Heisenberg's uncertainty principle, these properties cannot be measured precisely enough at the quantum level. String theory is a potential theory of everything since it takes into consideration gravitons, which we know are speculative particles that mediate the gravity force and allow gravitational interaction to be explained at the quantum level.

With the introduction of the supersymmetry principle, Bosonic string theory was superseded by theories called superstring theories and allowed to solve both the fermion and tachyon problems.

In particle physics, *supersymmetry* (SUSY) is a conjectured relationship between two basic classes of elementary particles; since nature is symmetric, every boson has a fermion superpartner, and every fermion has a boson superpartner. If string theory is combined with supersymmetry, superstring theory is created; when physicists refer to string theory, they generally refer to superstring theory, which describes all fermions and bosons as the result of a vibrating superstring of energy.

A supersymmetric theory would have its force equations identical to matter equations. For this reason, many physicists are attracted to the way supersymmetry relates force to matter and bosons to fermions, making the standard model more elegant. While many scientists appreciate supersymmetry, many others criticize this theory because no superpartner particles have been observed, and there is no particle accelerator large enough to test this theory.

Nonetheless, when supersymmetry is combined with general relativity, the supergravity theory generated seems incredibly elegant. Also, as mentioned before, supersymmetry has been applied to string theory, developing five superstring theories, each with ten total dimensions. These theories were initially found to be perturbative, with no single one with the potential to be a theory of everything, until Edward Witten joined the party. The American physicist noticed that the five-string theories could be mapped to one another by certain conditions known as *dualities*. Instead of being distinct theories, he suggested that they can be the cornerstone of a more fundamental theory, *m-theory*.

M-theory can be defined as a proposal for a unified quantum theory of nature's fundamental constituents and forces, containing superstring theories and supergravity. It has since been considered the best candidate for a theory of everything, even if it is not entirely refined yet and only its based principles are immutable:

- There are 11 dimensions in M-theory.

- It doesn't contain only one-dimensional strings but also other objects with a range of different dimensions, called P brains. Examples are three-dimensional blobs, two-dimensional sheets, four-dimensional hyper blobs, etc.

We can say that, while our universe has a particular way of shaping hyperspace and consequently certain laws of nature, the laws of m-theory allow other universes with different ways of shaping hyperspace and vastly different laws of nature. The multiverse idea is probably one of the most exciting concepts of m-theory and opens to unlimited possibilities; to know more, we will have to wait and see if this is the unified theory everyone is looking for or just another step during our journey.

4.5 Quantum Entanglement

Imagine ordering takeaway pizza for dinner; you take a Margherita while your partner wants a pepperoni. Thirty minutes later, the food is delivered to your door; you receive two identical pizza boxes. Until you open a box, you have no way of knowing which one contains your pizza.

Once you open one of the boxes and see a Margherita, you will immediately know that the other one has the pepperoni pizza; this means that the Margherita and the pepperoni are 'entangled' in a certain way. Quantum entanglement is based on a similar idea, only on a much smaller scale.

Formally, quantum entanglement is a physical phenomenon that occurs when a pair or group of particles is generated, interacts, or shares spatial proximity in a way such that the quantum state of each particle of the pair or group cannot be described independently of the state of the others, including when a large distance separates the particles.

In three-dimensional space, X, Y, and Z coordinates are used to specify an object's exact location, and it is known that two objects cannot have the same coordinates. If we include time (t), we are now in a four-dimensional space, but the same uniqueness principle applies, two objects cannot have the same four coordinates. In the same way, an electron is identified by four quantum numbers, and every electron has a unique set of these coordinates. These 'dimensions' are called:

- principal quantum number (n)

- orbital angular momentum quantum number (l)

- magnetic quantum number (m_l)

- electron spin quantum number (m_s)

These numbers are used to determine the electron configuration of an atom and the probable locations of the electrons. For the scope of this chapter, the most relevant of these parameters is the electron spin quantum number, the intrinsic value of the angular momentum of a fundamental particle.

Here is where quantum mechanics becomes counterintuitive another time. When we say that an electron has a positive or negative spin, it has angular momentum and magnetic orientation, but it is not actually spinning! Instead, the electron might exist in a superposition state when it has both a negative and positive spin. For example, when a coin spins on a flat surface, it is in a superposition state between its two faces (heads and tails); similarly, electrons in their natural state exist as a superposition of both up and down spin. Only when measured is it possible to understand which spin is applied.

When a pair of electrons are generated, interact, or share spatial proximity, their spin states can get entangled, which is what scientists call the quantum entanglement of electrons. Once two electrons are entangled, the two electrons can only have opposite spins. For example, if one is measured up spin, then we will immediately know that the second is down spin.

If we were to separate the two electrons and place them on the opposite side of the galaxy, measuring the spin of one of the two electrons will immediately know the measurement of the other, this information travels instantaneously and faster than the speed of light!

This effect was so disturbing and incredible that Einstein decided to call it "spooky action at a distance." In the following chapters, I will introduce real-world applications of the quantum entanglement principle and quantum physics.

~ Part 5 ~
Real-World Applications of Quantum Physics

5.1 Ultra-Precise Clocks

Since humans began tracking the passage of time, they have done so using periodic phenomena, such as the sun's motion across the sky; in modern times, vibrations in atoms are the most stable periodic events that scientists can observe.

Clocks are one of the most common everyday objects. Having a common synchronized clock is very important in today's world; they keep things like stock markets and GPS systems in line. In addition, atomic clocks are the most precise timekeepers we have today, with the best ones keeping time to within one second in 15 billion years.

They use lasers to measure the vibrations of atoms, which oscillate at a constant frequency, like many microscopic pendulums swinging in sync.

The most common element used in atomic clocks is the cesium-133 atom, which oscillates precisely 9,192,631,770 times per second, and it's so stable that this pattern has officially defined the second since 1968.

MIT Researchers have recently presented a new quantum-entangled atomic clock. This device uses laser technology to measure the oscillations of the atoms inside, and due to its incredible accuracy, it can be used to set national and international standards.

In general, quantum entanglement describes a non-classical physical state where atoms in a group show correlated measurement results, even though each atom behaves like a random toss of a coin (spin). To keep perfect time, clocks would ideally track the oscillations of a single atom. But, at that scale, an atom is so tiny that it behaves according to the mysterious rules of quantum mechanics; when measured, it acts like a flipped coin only when averaged. This limitation is what physicists refer to as the standard quantum limit.

The new MIT clock could push the boundaries of precision even further, despite the standard quantum limit. In fact, this new atomic clock does not measure a cloud of randomly oscillating atoms like other high precision clocks; instead, it measures atoms that have been quantumly entangled. As a result, the new setup can drastically reduce the quantum limit effect, achieving the same precision four times faster than clocks without entanglement.

When the number of entangled atoms increases, the average given by all these atoms goes toward something that gives the correct value; also, if atoms are entangled, their individual oscillations would tighten up around a standard frequency, with less deviation than if they were not entangled. Therefore, the average oscillations that an atomic clock would measure would have a precision beyond the standard quantum limit.

The researchers started with about 350 atoms of ytterbium-171, which oscillates even faster than cesium and at the same very high frequency as visible light. These atoms are trapped in an optical cavity between two mirrors; a laser is shone into the cavity to quantum entangle the particles. Once the atoms are entangled, a second laser is shone through the cloud to measure their average frequency. The researchers say that this method could make atomic clocks so precise that after the entire age of the universe, they would still be less than 100 milliseconds out of sync. Atomic clocks could be even more precise; if they could more accurately measure atomic vibrations, they would be sensitive enough to detect phenomena such as dark matter and gravitational waves. With better atomic clocks, scientists could also start to answer some mind-bending questions, such as what effect gravity might have on the passage of time and if time itself changes as the universe ages.

5.2 Quantum Key Distribution

Every time you buy something online or send a private Facebook message, how do you know that no one can see it? Of course, you don't, but you trust in the encryptions protecting it.

A widespread type of encryption is based on secret-key cryptography; this is where a message is scrambled using a key known only to the sender and receiver. Anyone can see the message, but no one can read it without the key. These keys can be hard to break depending on who has implemented them and for which service. What makes these codes practically unbreakable is the amount of time and computational resources required to crack the code. For example, if all the world's personal computers were working incessantly to break the code that keeps your Facebook login safe, it would take them around 12 million times the universe's age. But there is a new upcoming player, quantum computers, which would complete, in a few days, tasks that for modern computers would require billions of years. Obviously, this is just a theory, and quantum computers are not ready yet, but researchers are!

They have invented a new type of cryptography that even the quantum computer could not break. Quantum cryptography implements a new security paradigm; instead of math, it relies on the laws of quantum mechanics, more specifically on Heisenberg's uncertainty principle. If you recall, this principle states that you cannot know everything about the state of a quantum particle; you can measure the position or momentum but never both at the same time.

The first quantum cryptographic system was tried in 1989, and the key was sent for around two meters on a very short cable between two computers; now, a key can be sent kilometers away without corruption.

Let's say you want to send your friend Homer a private message which is encrypted using a classical encryption key. If you want your friend Homer to understand your message, the key will be sent on a secure line after the message is received. Doing so, if someone intercepts the message, they would not be able to understand it because they are missing the key to decrypt it. But, if an eavesdropper has tapped into the secure line and got in possession of the key, they would be able to decipher all the messages generated with that key, making the cryptographic process useless.

This scenario would never happen using *quantum key distribution* (QKD); in this case, the key is a stream of photons with a specific spin that can be changed when it passes through a filter.

Depending on the type of spin, a photon can be read as 1 or 0; four types of filters can be used to send strings of 1 and 0 using combinations of photons.

Yes, there are four filters to write 0 or 1, which means that there are two ways to write a 1 and two ways to write a 0. If someone tries to intercept the key, they will have to use the right filter not to change the spin of the photons, and since the sender typically generates a key randomly, the eavesdropper is likely to parse wrongly around half of the photons.

In this case, the laws of quantum physics prevent malicious people from intercepting the key, but how is Homer going to know which filter to use to read the key?

Well, the idea is to reach Homer and tell him which category of filter you have used:

- Rectilinear: can generate both 0 and 1 depending on the type

- Diagonal: can generate both 0 and 1 depending on the type

Scanning photon by photon, if Homer uses the correct filter (he will still have to choose among two, even knowing the category), you both keep the digit; if he chooses the wrong filter, then the digit is discarded. So, statistically, Homer will get half of the digits wrong. The remaining part is going to be your encryption key!

Ok, but what about a person that might listen to this conversation?

Listening will absolutely not help an attacker; let's say that for the first photon, you both used a rectilinear filter, and you keep the digit; the attacker used the wrong filter, and he won't be able to tell if it is a 1 or 0 from just which scheme we used. For the second photon, you used a diagonal filter, and so did the attacker, but Homer used a rectilinear filter, and for this reason, the digit is discarded. Basically, you will have in your hands a super-secure key while the attacker will have nothing. Quantum cryptography is different from any encryption system that we know of, and once implemented, it will make life very difficult for hackers worldwide.

5.3 Quantum Computing

We are all familiar with classic computers, and we know that they have enabled amazing things, but there are problems they cannot solve. They might be able to solve small versions of these problems, but classic computers start to run out of computational resources when problems begin to become interesting.

We can take, as an example, the process of finding the best solution to a problem among many possible solutions: optimization. Let's say you are out at dinner with nine friends, and you have to sit around a table. How many ways are there to place ten people around a table? The answer is ten factorial. You might think ten is small, but actually, ten factorial is 3.6 million combinations, and every time we add one person to the table, the number of possible configurations grows exponentially. A classical machine might be able to solve small versions of this problem, but it will soon reach its limits if the number of people is large enough.

Another example of problems not easily solved by classic computers relates to chemistry. If you try to simulate a molecule on a classical computer, you will have to account for every electron, electron repulsion, and every attraction of the electrons of the nuclei. The number of interactions in a molecule grows exponentially with its size; the simulation will quickly push a supercomputer to its limits just after a few simulated atoms.

There are a lot of problems that have similar characteristics, and they all have in common the fact that their complexity scales exponentially with the size of the problem.

So why is quantum computing different? Why should quantum computing allow scientists to solve problems that supercomputers cannot?

Quantum computers can do what other computers cannot due to two fundamental quantum effects.

The first effect we are going to consider is superposition. Classical computers use memory made up of bits. Bits speak to possibly one or zero, on or off. Everything computers do, from messing around to sending an email, originates from controlling those ones and zeros. So classical information is basically a string of zeros and ones.

Quantum information has the property that the states can exist in a superposition of 0 and 1; this allows for exploring a much richer set of states. Also, this property allows to have complex superpositions, if a quantum bit (qubit) can be in a superposition of two states, then two qubits can be in a superposition of four states, and three qubits can be in a superposition of eight states, and so on. This allows us to describe many complex states. Consequently, we can say that quantum information is richer than classical binary information.

The second effect we must consider is entanglement; if we take two qubits and entangle them together when we measure the first qubit, the result will tell us something about what will happen when we measure the second qubit. Basically, the states of entangled qubits cannot be described independently of each other. This second property makes quantum information peculiar and utterly different from the binary information we are used to.

Combining these two properties completely changes how algorithms are executed on quantum computers.

If we take the case of configuring ten people around a table, the classic approach will consider every possible case individually and then compare all the results. However, in quantum computing, we place our qubits in a superposition of all the possible configurations. Then, when the problem is encoded in the machine, a phase is applied to every state. At that point, interference is used to amplify some answers and cancel other answers, allowing the device to arrive at the solution.

I know this example is not exhaustive but describing how algorithms work on quantum computers is not the aim of this book for beginners. Here, I'm just trying to give you the fundamental concepts and stimulate your curiosity.

If I have aroused your interest, there are countless books dedicated to quantum computing that can help you explore the topic in more detail!

Going back to our example, it seems that quantum computers' power is based on the number of qubits available to encode a specific state, right?

This is not entirely true; another important factor we must consider is the error rate. It is crucial to have complete control of the behavior of the qubit. Having a high error rate will imply that operations executed on a quantum computer, in some cases, will not produce the expected results, impacting the calculations. For this reason, a metric called quantum volume is taken into consideration. This metric shows that increasing the number of qubits will lead to higher computational power, but not in the presence of elevated error rates.

There is also another peculiar characteristic of quantum computers called coherence time. Quantum information, currently, doesn't live in the quantum world forever; it usually lasts just a few hundreds of microseconds before it is lost. This determines the number of operations it is possible to run before your information is lost, and quantum developers must consider this factor.

This is cool but very theoretical. So how do we build a quantum computer?

The first element we must consider is the qubit; it is required to have an element that behaves like an artificial atom where properties of quantum mechanics apply. These artificial atoms are generally created from a Josephson Junction coupled to a microwave resonator. The temperature also plays an important role; the main quantum computer chip must cool down to -460 degrees Fahrenheit to properly work. For comparison, -460 degrees Fahrenheit is colder than outer space temperature, which is -454 degrees Fahrenheit.

To interact with the qubits, microwaves are used to flip their state.

You might now think that quantum computers are big and cold machines, stored in secret superlabs and accessible only to a tiny elite of scientists. It is true that to see a quantum computer physically, you might have to go to a lab, but everyone can access one.

IBM has recently released IBM Quantum Experience that allows to access and play a quantum computer on the cloud: https://quantum-computing.ibm.com

This allows all the inquisitive people to try this exciting new technology and help develop it.

Conclusion

Maybe, indeed certainly, I will repeat myself a little bit, but, as you know by now, this is one of my 'strategies' of divulgation, which many people appreciate and, therefore, I keep doing it.

First, let me make one observation that is certainly not new to you. Quantum Mechanics (QM) was born in the same years as the theory of relativity and was, in a similar way, a reference theory for the whole 20th century. However, it has never really been able to get out of the narrow circle of insiders. One might think this is due to the mathematical difficulties of the expressions that govern the wave function and not only complex planes and similar things. But, no, it is not enough to explain its 'ghettoization.'

There must be something else that seems to preclude its disclosure. Relativity is no less than that, but it has entered overwhelmingly into ordinary language. Moreover, QM is at the basis of all the technological innovations of today, from atomic energy to computer microelectronics, from digital clocks to lasers, semiconductor systems, photoelectric cells, diagnostic and treatment equipment for many diseases. In short, today, we can 'live' in a 'modern' way thanks to QM and its applications.

Our mind seems to be based on quantum processes, including state overlaps, the wave collapses, and entanglement situations. The real difficulty lies in its 'counterintuitive' postulates about the reality of Nature. A real discomfort in entering an unknown and absurd world like Alice's. Let's not feel too inferior, though... The founding fathers themselves lived this situation to the limit of the absurd. Could one really believe that Nature followed completely arbitrary rules or, instead, was it all an appearance due to the lack of information, of a deterministic kind, still missing?

The very creator of the very general and ultra-confirmed principle of indeterminacy (Heisenberg) said, "I remember the long discussions with Bohr, which made us stay up late at night and left us in a state of deep depression, not to say real despair. I kept walking alone in the park, and I kept thinking that it was impossible that Nature was as absurd as it appeared to us from the experiments,". In a nutshell, there is no defined and describable reality but an objectively indistinct reality composed of superimposed states.

Let's pick up on two essential points that we have learned but certainly don't understand:

- Every action of the finer structure of matter is characterized only by its probability of happening. Phenomena are completely acausal, not deterministic. But, above all, by the indistinct separation between the observed object, the measuring instrument, and the observer.

- It is possible that, under certain conditions, what happens in a certain place can drastically influence what happens in a completely different place instantly. This leads to the phenomenon of entanglement, the twisting of particles that have had an interaction in their past (but recent research also seems to admit 'contacts' in the future) or that were born 'together.' Although completely separate, they always represent the same entity. An action performed on one has an instantaneous effect on the other.

Perhaps you've already noticed the real problem with the QM. On the one hand, the difficulty of dealing with concepts that are too far removed from everyday reality, and on the other hand, the difficulty of using proper language to explain this absurd world. Math can also describe it, but the letters and words of this strange alphabet are missing. It is interesting to quote a sentence by Max Born about this (1957):

> The ultimate origin of the difficulty lies in the fact (or philosophical principle) that we are compelled to use the words of common language when we wish to describe a phenomenon, not by logical or mathematical analysis, but by a picture appealing to the imagination. Common language has grown by everyday experience and can never surpass these limits. Classical physics has restricted itself to the use of concepts of this kind; by analyzing visible motions it has developed two ways of representing them by elementary processes: moving particles and waves. There is no other way of giving a pictorial description of motions – we have to apply it even in the region of atomic processes, where classical physics breaks down, (1957), 97.

In a nutshell, the description of the QM itself could be heavily influenced by our 'classic' descriptive limits.

Therefore, the founding fathers often used analogies and similarities to express purely mathematical concepts. They, however, must be considered for what they are and should not be given any real and concrete validity. This is a massive problem for our brain (especially today) even if—perhaps—it would have all the basics to use an adequate language, but still too indistinct to be formulated correctly.

Niels Bohr used graphic analogies to try to support such absurd theories for our classical language. Famous is the white vase representing two black human profiles at the same time.

A state of superimposition between two realities existing instantly (two states or—maybe two Universes?). This analogy has influenced many optical illusion games and even artistic currents (think of Picasso).

Fig.9 - Optical illusion where it is possible to see both a vase and two profiles at the same time.

It is a pity that these interpretative efforts, combined with Feynman's more complete and refined efforts, do not find their way into schools to adequately prepare young people to 'stammer' their first quantum words and begin a primitive language that would allow them to understand, at least partially, the reality of Alice and not only passively undergo the most wonderful technological applications that are now an integral part of their physical body. Real 'appendages' act unconsciously, independently of any mental command. Unconditional reflexes and nothing more.

After all, de Broglie advanced his daring hypothesis precisely by following the symmetries of visible Nature. He only associated with the matter in general, what happened to the light. In short: If light manifests itself under a double aspect, undulating and corpuscular, why not think that matter also follows the same rule? It is enough to associate to each corpuscle of matter a wave of a certain length, that is, a phenomenon extended to the space surrounding the particle. The dualistic nature (particle waves) applies to all particles, such as electrons, atoms, and other moving entities.

However, the fundamental problem remains open (still today, the subject of discussion and interpretation), which we have mentioned. The wave of matter that commands the particle can be deterministic and therefore still unknown in its real structure (in line with Einstein's idea) or, instead, a different representation of the same particle and thus follows the rules of complete causality (Copenhagen school).

In one way or another, however, it must be concluded that the light or a beam of electrons is nothing but a 'train' of electromagnetic waves, but also a jet of 'bullets' as in the double-slit experiment.

While remaining in this basic ambiguity, Schrödinger formulated the equation that perfectly describes every undulatory property of matter through its wave function. It allows us to describe every single behavior and, above all, to calculate the probability distribution to find a particle inside the associated wave. However, overwhelming mathematics does not annul the fact that Schrödinger himself did not believe in the actual concreteness of this representation. A particle can occupy ALL possible positions within the associated wave. By occupying all possible positions, it no longer has an actual place of existence or direction. It automatically cancels any possible prediction of its future, except in purely probabilistic terms (the QED is increasingly understandable... don't you think?). The pilot wave or a hidden variable does not change the action of Nature and its probabilistic description.

Once again, we fall back on Heisenberg's principle... In classical mechanics, deterministic essence automatically allows you to predict the future if you have exact information about the position and speed of a particle. Let us remember, in this regard, that the first mathematical methods that allowed the calculation of an orbit of a 'planetary' particle were based (and still are based) on the knowledge of at least three positions and three velocities, such as to allow the solution of an orbit characterized by six unknowns. Too easy for microscopic particles.

The probabilistic conception leads inexorably to the principle of indeterminacy, inherent in the whole microcosm: Either one knows the position or one knows the speed. To know both with accuracy is impossible. Otherwise, the particle would be located, and the wave would collapse. And we go back to the starting point again—whether there is an initial causality (completely unknown) or not at all. In a nutshell, the double-slit experiment perfectly illustrates all the problems of QM.

It's worth reflecting on Einstein's dramatic emotional situation. While he was giving physical reality a perfectly deterministic representation, he found himself involved in a representation that led to the complete causality of Nature. He said:

> Quantum radiation theories interest me very much, but I wouldn't want to be forced to abandon narrow causality without trying to defend it to the limit. I find the idea quite intolerable that an electron exposed to radiation should choose its own free will, not only its moment to jump off but its direction. In that case, I would rather be a cobbler, or even an employee in a gaming house, than a physicist.

CPSIA information can be obtained
at www.ICGtesting.com
Printed in the USA
LVHW022314251122
733804LV00005B/250